It's Shapes and Sizes Day! Blue is looking  and sizes around her house. Will you help special decoder included in this book. Use it to see the answers hidden next to Blue's pawprints.

1

First Blue wants to find toys that are shaped like a circle .
That's a round shape with no sides or corners.
Look, Blue found a ball!

Do you see any other toys that are shaped like a circle?
Color them and use the decoder to check your answers.

Tickety also has a circle shape. Do you see it?

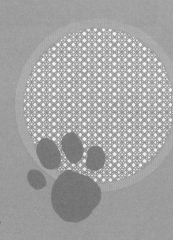

Now Blue wants to find a square ☐. A square has four sides that are all the same length. Trace the sides of the toys that have the square shape.

A rectangle  has four sides just like a square, but two sides are long and two are short. Mark an **X** on the toy that is shaped like a rectangle.

Great job, Shape Finder!

5

A triangle  has three sides that can be any length. Will you help Blue find the toy that has the triangle shape? Terrific! Circle it and look next to Blue's pawprint to see if you're right.

Hey, Shape Finder! Circles, squares, rectangles, and triangles are everywhere! Find and trace these shapes on Slippery's boat.

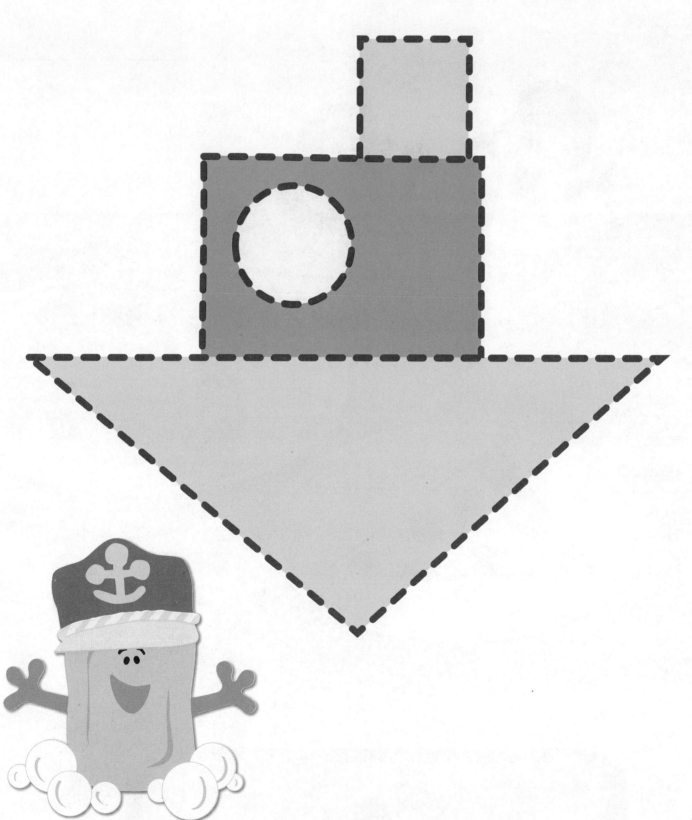

Maybe Blue can find some more shapes in the kitchen. Do you see any triangle-shaped snacks? Trace them.

How many did you find? _____

How many snacks are shaped
like a rectangle?

_____

- - - - - - - - - - - - - - - -

_____

Trace them.

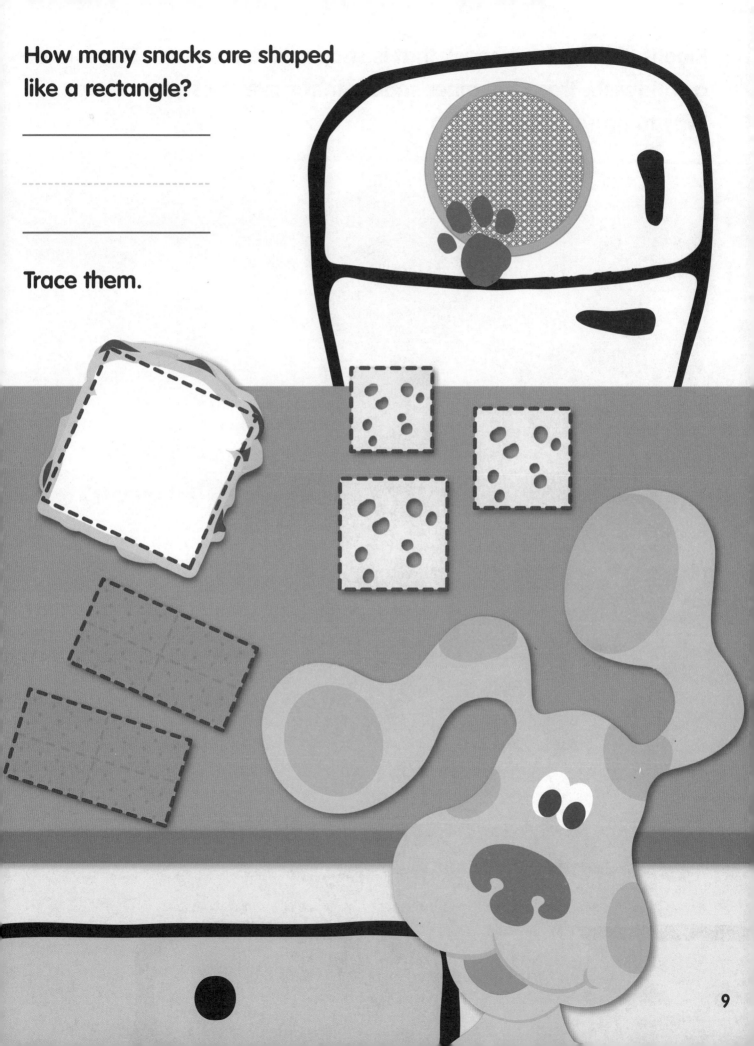

Blue is looking for a snack that is shaped like a square. She found a sandwich. Trace the other snacks that have the square shape. Way to go!

The rest of the snacks are shaped like circles.

How many circle snacks do you see?

_____

_____

Trace them.

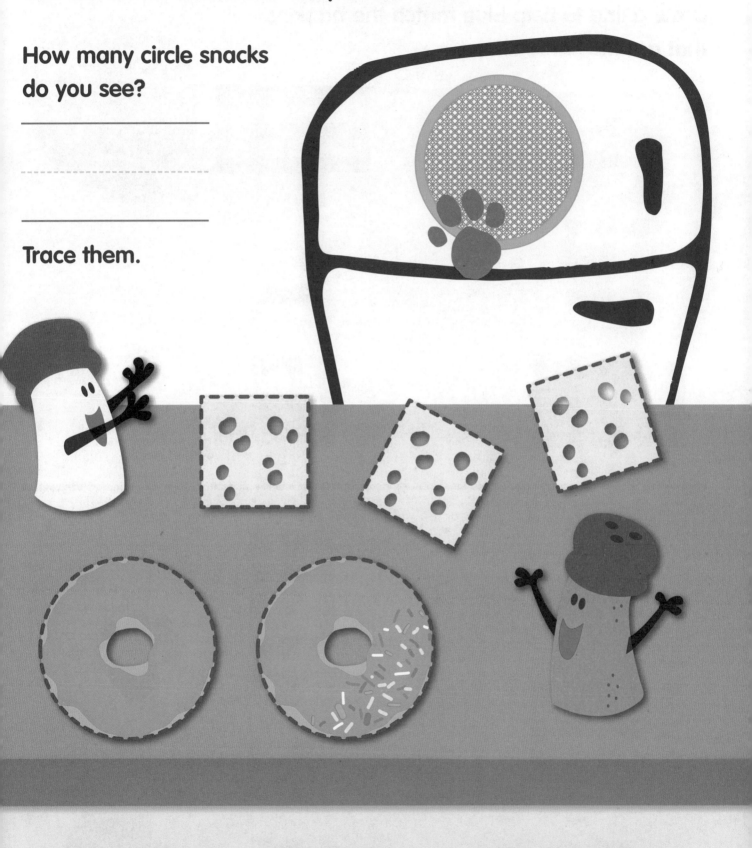

Draw a line to help Blue match the napkins
that are the same shape.

Are you ready to help Blue find some sizes? Okay, Size Finder, Blue has three melons and she wants to find the biggest one. Will you color it for her?

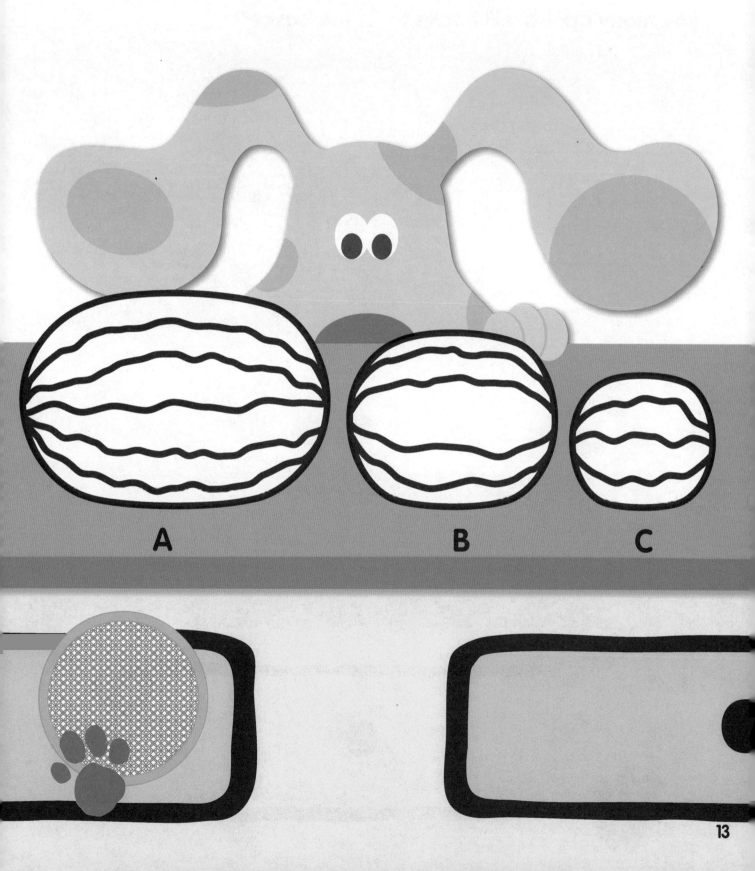

A   B   C

Mr. Salt and Mrs. Pepper have three piles of apples. Blue wants to find the pile that will fit exactly in her basket. It's the smallest pile. Will you circle the smallest pile to show Blue?

How many apples will it take to fill the basket?

_____

- - - - - - - - - - - - - - - -

_____

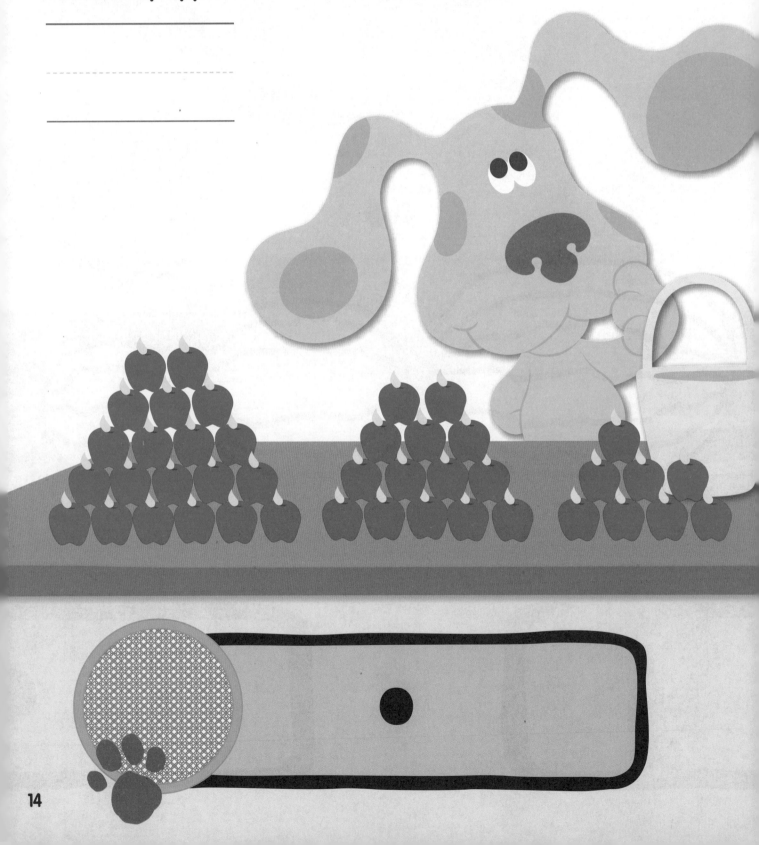

Great work, Size Finder! Now will you color the bigger bunch of grapes for Blue?

How many grapes are in the bunch?

_____

- - - - - - - - - - - - -

_____

Now Blue wants to find the longest loaf of bread. Circle the letter below the longest loaf and use your decoder to check your answer.

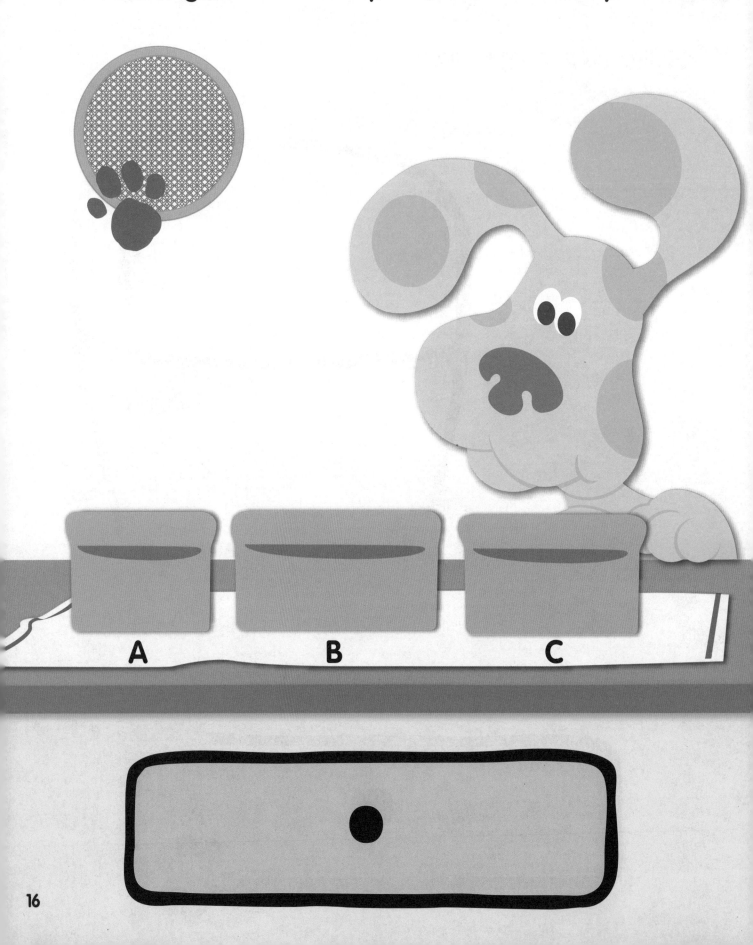

A   B   C

Look closely at the shapes and sizes and help Blue by drawing what comes next.

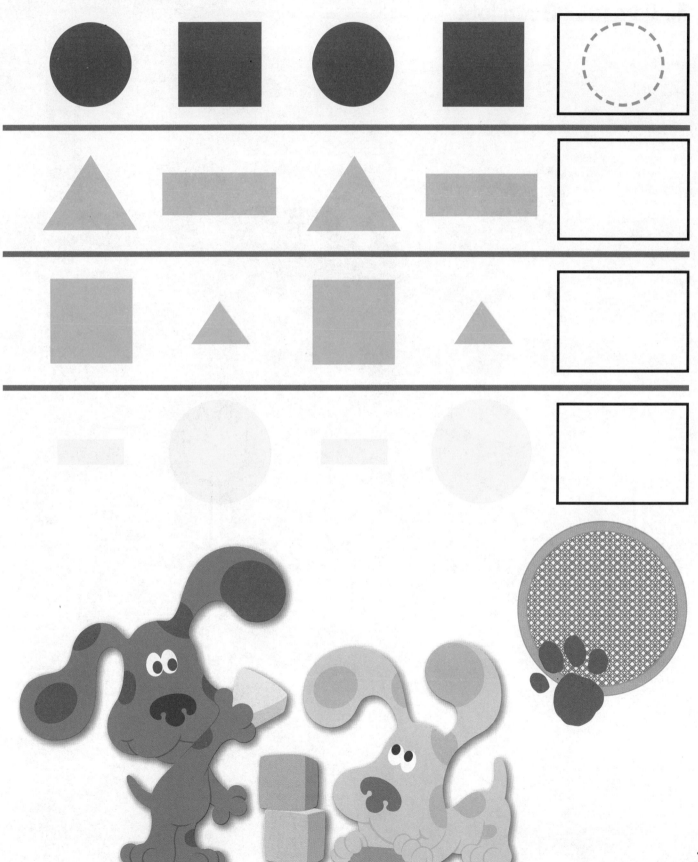

Blue is looking for more sizes in the garden. She sees short flowers and tall flowers. Will you color the short flowers blue and the tall flowers red? Good job!

Mrs. Pepper loves flowers! Blue wants to find the tallest flower to give her. Do you see it? Circle it.

Look, Pail and Shovel are helping Blue find sizes. They found some long and short inchworms crawling in the garden. Circle the short ones.

_____

How many short inchworms are there?

_____

Draw a line from each tree to the one that's the same size and shape.

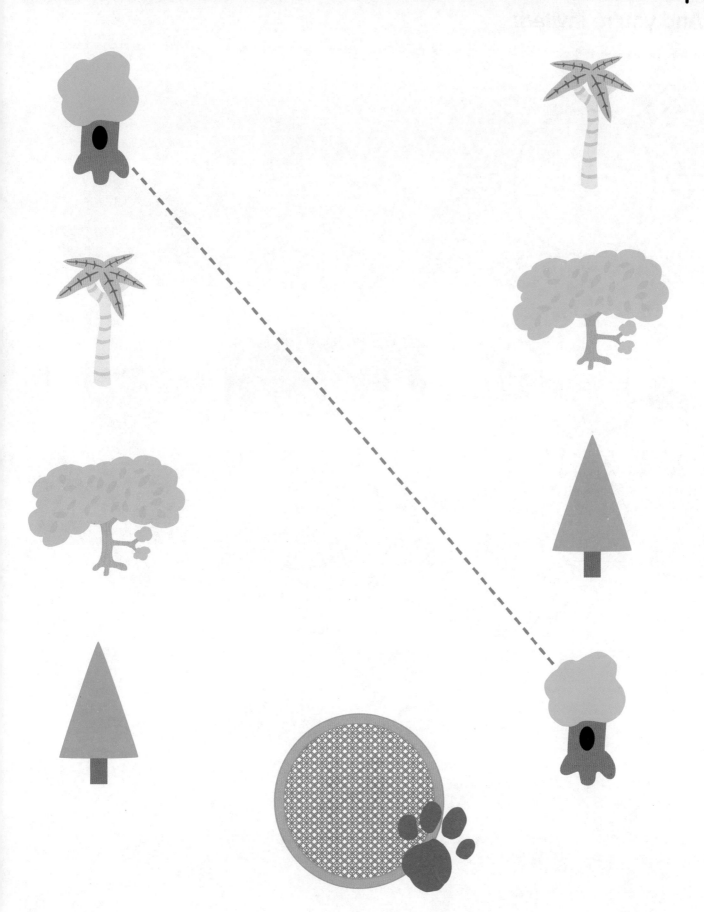

You helped Blue find so many shapes and sizes. Now Blue wants to have a Shapes and Sizes Party with her friends. And you're invited!

Find and trace the shapes. Then color them using the color code.

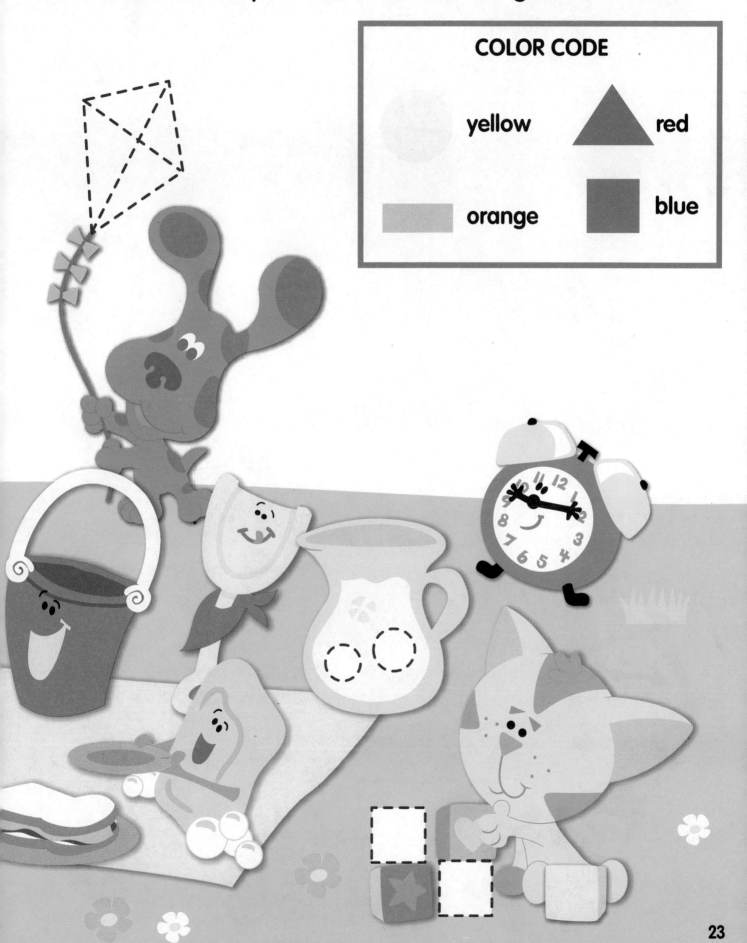

COLOR CODE

yellow

red

orange

blue

23

Great job, Shapes and Sizes Finder!